For NEVAEH ABERCROMBIE (the Sugar Plum Fairy) and her Mummy SOPHIE (the Dancing Queen!)

HODDER CHILDREN'S BOOKS in association with FOX AND HOUND ANIMATION STUDIOS
present an ALEX T. SMITH PRODUCTION.

starring

VIVIEN VIXEN *and* MARLON BITEHARD

in

CATCH US IF YOU CAN-CAN

co-starring

HEN GOODMAN * CRAIG REVEL-HERON * ALESHA CHICKSON * BRUNO TOUCAN-INI

With special thanks to Sylvia Bird and all the dancers from the 'Shake Your Tail Feathers' Dance, Music and Theatre School.

Director ALEX T. SMITH Editor EMMA LAYFIELD Production Designer ALISON STILL
Production Manager CHRISTINA HARRISON Eggs-ecutive Producers ALISON ELDRED | ANNE McNEIL
Choreographer JENNIFER HEN-DLEY Best Boys ANDREW NOLAN | ANDREW SHARP
Bird Wranglers TAMLYN FRANCIS | CAROLINE THOMSON | MICHELLE DANSO

First released in 2012 by Hodder Children's Books
Text and illustrations copyright © Alex T. Smith 2012

Produced by Hodder Children's Books,
338 Euston Road, London NW1 3BH.
In association with Hodder Children's Books Australia,
Level 17/207 Kent Street, Sydney, NSW 2000.

Written and Illustrated in York, UK
and at Hodder Children's Books Studios, London

This book is based on true events, however, some of the
characters, names and certain locations and events have
been changed, and others have been fictionalized for
dramatization purposes. No chickens, birds or eggs were
harmed in the production of this book, however the author
and his associates do admit that some of the dance shoes
worn by the cast did pinch a bit and caused some blisters.

ISBN: 9781 444 903 652
10 9 8 7 6 5 4 3 2 1

Hodder Children's Books is a division of Hachette
Children's Books. An Hachette UK Company.
www.hachette.co.uk

*Hodder
Children's
Books*

Hodder Children's Books presents

A book by

ALEX T. SMITH

CATCH US IF YOU CAN-CAN

Vivien Vixen *as* FOXY DuBOIS *and* Marlon Bitehard *as* ALPHONSO

Let me introduce you to Foxy Dubois,
a fox with big ideas, and Alphonso,
an alligator with attitude.

This is the story about how, one day, it all
went horribly wrong for them both.

It had all started a week before.
Foxy DuBois was down on her
luck. She had no job, no home,
and no matter how much
she shook her piggy bank,
it wouldn't give up a dime.

'I've gotta hit the big time!'
she said to herself. 'But how?'

It was right at that moment that something caught her eye...

BIRDS OF A FEATHER
DANCE TROUPE
presents

SO YOU THINK YOU CAN BOOGIE?

Come shake your tail feathers this
Friday at the Cock-a-doodle Ballroom
on Nesting Lane at 7.30pm

Prize for the best couple:
A Giant Golden EGG!

SMALL PRINT: COMPETITION OPEN TO BIRDS ONLY

But there was a hitch, the competition was only open to birds. 'Foiled already!' thought Foxy. But as she wandered through the dark streets of the Big City, she hatched a cunning plan...

For her idea to work, she needed a dance partner. Alphonso was the most dastardly alligator in the whole world, but he had the daintiest dancing feet she knew!

She dialled A for Alligator.

'Imagine what we could do with that Golden Egg!' she said in a voice as gooey as a soft-boiled yolk. 'We would be rich!'

It didn't take long to convince him.

There was no time to lose!
The next morning they picked up their disguises from
the fancy dress shop, brushed up on their dance skills,
and rehearsed until their feet could dance no more.

When the big day arrived,
they were ready for action!

The competition was fierce.
But Foxy and Alphonso were fiercer.
They plucked the other contestants
off the dance floor, one by one!

Until, at last, it
was time for
their turn...

They were brilliant.
The judges had never
seen anything as good as
this in all their lives.
The Golden Egg was theirs.

But it was too good to be true. It only took one high kicking spin and...

...their costumes fell off!
There were feathers
everywhere!

'A FOX!?'

cried a can-can chicken.

'AN ALLIGATOR?!'

cried a dapper dancing duck.

'LOOK, THEY'RE
IN THEIR PANTS!'

cried a pirouetting penguin.

It was time to scarper.

THE BIG CITY

DESERT

DANGER

VERY
HIGH
CLIFF

They sped off through the night;
Foxy with her paw to the floor.
But hot on their heels were the judges!

'Let's get outta here!'
cried Foxy and she drove off...

...the side of a cliff! Weeeeeeeeeeeeeeeeeeeeeeeeeeeeee!

But don't worry, Foxy had one last trick up her sleeve.

When they landed safely
they stopped to look at
the Giant Golden Egg.

'It's ours!' cried Foxy. 'We're rich!
Rich beyond our wildest dreams.
We've finally hit the big time.'
And she threw the Egg high
into the air with joy!

But Foxy had never
been a good catch...

The Egg hit the floor and
smashed into a million
delicious pieces!

'Chocolate?!' shouted Alphonso. 'A CHOCOLATE EGG?!
You've strung me along, Foxy! I should have gobbled
you up when I had the chance!'

'I'm getting outta here!' cried Foxy. 'See you later, alligator.'

And she quickstepped away back to the Big City, once again
escaping the jaws of the dastardly Alphonso.

The End